First Mental Arithmetic 6

Answers

Ann Montague-Smith

Schofield & Sims

Teacher's notes

The format of *First Mental Arithmetic* differs from that of traditional mental arithmetic materials in that the children read the questions themselves and write down their answers. The individual books may be used flexibly and children may set their own pace. However, you might find it helpful to use one book per term.

The mathematical content of the *First Mental Arithmetic* activities should already have been covered in maths lessons and the reading content is kept simple. Nevertheless, you might consider asking a classroom assistant to work with a group of children, helping them to read the questions. Ask the assistant to note the names of children needing further help, and the activities or concepts that they find difficult. You can then provide the necessary teaching, support or additional practice.

Books 4 to 6

Books 4 to 6 are designed for Year 2 but are also suitable for some older children. Each book is split into three sections. The sections are divided into sessions, each comprising one page of 30 questions. Parts A, B and C of each session contain different question types; for further details, please see the back cover. Depending on the child's skills, a session's work may be completed during the course of a week or over whatever time span you feel is appropriate.

As the children progress, different levels of support are provided. By the time they reach Books 4 to 6, the children will know some key maths facts. If they cannot recall these, they should be aware of strategies that will help them to find answers. Children needing more help may find a number line useful – either an actual line or one that they visualise.

Encourage the children to use the following mental strategies when working through Book 6.

- For addition and subtraction: using known facts to help them to find the answer. (For example, from $6 + 3 = 9$, they can work out that $36 + 3 = 39$; from $9 - 4 = 5$, they can deduce that $9 - 5 = 4$.)
- For finding the difference: counting up from the smaller to the larger number. (For example, for the difference between 19 and 21, they count up, 19 to 20, then one more to 21.)
- For multiplication: knowing the basic multiplication facts.
- For division: recognising that if they know $5 \times 2 = 10$, they can deduce that $10 \div 2 = 5$ and $10 \div 5 = 2$.
- For fractions: using squared paper to model the problem. (For example, for finding ¾ of 12, they would mark out a grid of 12 squares, find ½, then find ¼ or ½ of ½, then find ¾.)

Assessment

- Sessions 11 and 12 at the end of each section test all the concepts and facts covered in that section.
- Check-ups test children's understanding of *Shape and space* and *Handling data*.
- As children write their answers to the *Just facts* tests, they will notice helpful patterns. *Just facts* in Book 6 covers pairs that make 20, doubles to 20, and multiplication and division facts for 2s, 5s and 10s.

Record keeping

At the beginning of each workbook section is a photocopiable *Achievement chart* for completion by the child. In this book of answers, the *Achievement charts* are replaced by photocopiable *Group record sheets*, which allow you to note achievements and learning needs for each child. For example, you might write: *Knows multiplication facts for 2* or *Needs practice in writing number family facts*. Alternatively, you can simply record the child's marks. Use the completed sheets to plan appropriate work.

Children who have successfully completed *First Mental Arithmetic Book 6* may move on to *Mental Arithmetic Introductory Book*, obtainable separately from Schofield & Sims.

Contents

Section 1 Group record sheet

Class _____

Name	Read and write numbers to 1000 in figures and words Session 1	Sequences of numbers Session 1	Order two-digit numbers and position them on a number line Session 2	Use symbols < and > Session 2	Add and subtract a two-digit number and a one-digit number Session 3	Add and subtract a two-digit number to/from a multiple of ten Session 5	Addition and subtraction for numbers to 20 Session 6	Multiplication and division facts for 2s Session 9

From: **First Mental Arithmetic 6 Answers** by Ann Montague-Smith (ISBN 978 07217 1174 4). Copyright © Schofield & Sims Ltd, 2011. Published by Schofield & Sims Ltd, Dogley Mill, Fenay Bridge, Huddersfield HD8 0NQ, UK (www.schofieldandsims.co.uk). This page may be photocopied for use within your school or institution only.

Section 1 Session 1

Session Focus
Read and write numbers to 1000 in figures and words
Sequences of numbers

A   ANSWER

Write these numbers in figures.

1	Two hundred and thirty-six	236
2	Four hundred and nine	409
3	Seven hundred and ninety	790
4	Eight hundred and eighty-eight	888
5	One hundred and four	104

Write the missing numbers.

6	16	17	18	19		20
7	21	23	25	27		29
8	32	34	36	38		40
9	16	26	36	46		56
10	15	20	25	30		35

B   ANSWER

Write these numbers as words.

1 **246**
> two hundred and forty-six

2 **550**
> five hundred and fifty

3 **907**
> nine hundred and seven

4 **970**
> nine hundred and seventy

5 **444**
> four hundred and forty-four

Start at

6	**59**. Count back **3** tens.	29
7	**44**. Count on **4** tens.	84
8	**93**. Count back **3** ones.	90
9	**42**. Count on **8** twos.	58
10	**19**. Count on **7** tens.	89

C   ANSWER

What is the

1	tens digit in **432**?	3
2	hundreds digit in **927**?	9
3	units digit in **357**?	7

Write

4   one more than **899** in words.
> nine hundred

5   one less than **650** in words.
> six hundred and forty-nine

Here are some numbers

36   38   40   42

Write the number that comes

6	next.	44
7	before **36**.	34
8	two places before **36**.	32
9	three places after **42**.	48
10	ten places after **42**.	62

Section 1 Session 2

Session Focus
Order two-digit numbers and position them on a number line
Use symbols < and >

A   ANSWER

Use < or > to make these number sentences true.

1	54 65	<
2	92 45	>
3	45 54	<
4	36 63	<
5	92 29	>

Write the number where it belongs on the number line.

6   45   40 |——————45——————| 50

7   42   40 |——42——————————| 50

8   49   40 |——————————————49| 50

9   47   40 |——————————47————| 50

10   44   40 |————44——————————| 50

B   ANSWER

Use each number in the list just once to answer the questions.

35   92   36   45   60

1	45 <	60
2	92 >	45
3	< 36	35

| 4 | 44 > | 36 |
| 5 | > 60 | 92 |

Find the number that is in the wrong place.

6	45 46 48 47	E.g.	48
7	32 38 34 36		38
8	91 90 88 89	E.g.	88
9	12 32 22 42	E.g.	32
10	61 65 63 67	E.g.	65

C   ANSWER

What number is

1	1 greater than **45**?	46
2	10 less than **45**?	35
3	5 less than **67**?	62
4	3 more than **67**?	70
5	10 more than **89**?	99
6	2 more than **98**?	100

Here is Mark's homework.
Has he used the correct symbols?

Tick the correct answers.

Write the correct symbol if Mark is wrong.

7	36 < 45	✓
8	45 < 42	>
9	64 > 46	✓
10	92 > 93	<

Section 1 Session 3

Session Focus
Add and subtract a two-digit number and a one-digit number

A

			ANSWER
1	19 + 1	=	20
2	16 + 5	=	21
3	7 + 11	=	18
4	18 + 7	=	25
5	13 + 9	=	22
6	19 – 8	=	11
7	13 – 7	=	6
8	21 – 8	=	13
9	32 – 4	=	28
10	25 – 6	=	19

B

		ANSWER
1	___ + 5 = 21	16
2	___ + 17 = 21	4
3	13 + ___ = 22	9
4	16 + ___ = 23	7
5	___ + 16 = 24	8
6	23 – ___ = 17	6
7	26 – ___ = 17	9
8	___ – 5 = 28	33
9	___ – 7 = 42	49
10	___ – 6 = 44	50

C

ANSWER

34 grapes
Tom

27 raisins
Zehra

38 sultanas
Mark

Write how many are left.

		ANSWER
1	Tom eats **8** grapes.	26
2	Zehra eats **5** raisins.	22
3	Mark eats **9** sultanas.	29
4	Peter eats another **7** grapes.	19
5	Niamh eats another **6** raisins.	16
6	Sam eats another **9** sultanas.	20

How many

		ANSWER
7	grapes have been eaten altogether?	15
8	raisins have been eaten altogether?	11
9	sultanas have been eaten altogether?	18
10	fruits have been eaten in total?	44

7

Section 1   Session 4

A ANSWER

1 $(14) + \bullet\bullet\bullet$ $=$ 21

2 $(23) + \bullet\bullet\bullet$ $=$ 32

3 $(47) + \bullet\bullet\bullet$ $=$ 50

4 $(64) + \bullet\bullet\bullet$ $=$ 69

5 $(88) + \bullet\bullet\bullet$ $=$ 94

6 17 – 8 $=$ 9

7 23 – 4 $=$ 19

8 36 – 8 $=$ 28

9 56 – 9 $=$ 47

10 32 – 4 $=$ 28

B ANSWER

1 44 add 7 equals 51

2 56 add 4 is 60

3 64 subtract 9 leaves 55

4 72 minus 8 equals 64

5 37 and 4 is 41

6 97 add 3 equals 100

7 65 subtract 8 leaves 57

8 21 subtract 9 equals 12

9 55 add 7 equals 62

10 55 subtract 6 equals 49

C ANSWER

1 The difference between 72 and 3 is 69

2 How many more is 91 than 88? 3

3 How many fewer is 36 than 40? 4

What is the change from **50p**?

50p

4 Spend 6p. 44p

5 Spend 7p. 43p

Total

6 46p and 5p. 51p

7 72p and 9p. 81p

How much

8 less is 7p than 45p? 38p

9 more is 44p than 35p? 9p

10 What is the sum of 78p and 5p? 83p

8

Section 1   Session 5

A   ANSWER

1	$50 + 12$	$=$	62
2	$13 + 40$	$=$	53
3	$64 + 20$	$=$	84
4	$31 + 50$	$=$	81
5	$73 + 20$	$=$	93
6	$91 - 10$	$=$	81
7	$82 - 40$	$=$	42
8	$64 - 30$	$=$	34
9	$45 - 40$	$=$	5
10	$62 - 30$	$=$	32

B   ANSWER

1	$64 + \boxed{} = 70$	6
2	$50 + \boxed{} = 62$	12
3	$84 - \boxed{} = 70$	14
4	$92 - \boxed{} = 70$	22
5	$36 + \boxed{} = 56$	20
6	$24 - \boxed{} = 4$	20
7	$34 + \boxed{} = 84$	50
8	$63 + \boxed{} = 93$	30
9	$\boxed{} + 26 = 46$	20
10	$\boxed{} - 70 = 16$	86

C   ANSWER

How much is

1	**32p** and **50p**?	82 p
2	**80p** and **13p**?	93 p

What is left from

3	**95p** if you spend **45p**?	50 p
4	**90p** if you spend **72p**?	18 p

40cm

36cm

54cm

30cm

70cm

25cm

Find the total.

5	**40cm** and **36cm**.	76 cm
6	**54cm** and **30cm**.	84 cm
7	**70cm** and **25cm**.	95 cm
8	**50ml** and **45ml**.	95 ml
9	Subtract **80g** from **95g**.	15 g
10	What is the difference between **80g** and **65g**?	15 g

Section 1 Session 6

Session Focus
Addition and subtraction for numbers to 20

A   ANSWER

1   (11) + ●●● =   20
      ●●●
      ●●●

2   $12 + = 20$ 8

3   $15 + = 20$ 5

4   $ + 1 = 20$ 19

5   $ + 13 = 20$ 7

6   (20) − ●●● =   13
      ●●●
      ●

7   $20 - 18 = $ 2

8   $20 - 15 = $ 5

9   $20 - = 14$ 6

10   $20 - = 8$ 12

B   ANSWER

1   $20 = 13 + $ 7

2   $20 = + 9$ 11

3   $20 = 16 + $ 4

4   $20 = 11 + $ 9

5   $20 = + 17$ 3

6   $20 = + 14$ 6

7   $20 = 5 + $ 15

8   $20 = 19 + $ 1

9   $20 = 2 + $ 18

10   $20 = 10 + $ 10

C   ANSWER

What is the change from **20p** if you spend

1   **7p**?   13p

2   **14p**?   6p

3   **18p**?   2p

4   **11p**?   9p

5   **16p**?   4p

6   **3p**?   17p

7   **8p**?   12p

8   **1p**?   19p

9   **4p**?   16p

10   nothing?   20p

Section 1 Session 7

A   ANSWER

1   = 9

2   = 13

3   = 17

4   = 10

5   = 12

6 12 − 7 = 5

7 14 − 8 = 6

8 15 − 6 = 9

9 19 − 10 = 9

10 13 − 5 = 8

B   ANSWER

1 4 +   = 12   8

2 7 +   = 15   8

3 8 +   = 11   3

4   + 4 = 13   9

5   + 9 = 15   6

6 13 −   = 6   7

7 15 −   = 8   7

8   − 6 = 7   13

9   − 3 = 9   12

10 16 −   = 9   7

C   ANSWER

What is the total?

1 **6** boys and **8** girls.   14

2 **9** oranges and **10** apples.   19

3 **3** girls and another **8** girls.   11

4 **5** dogs and **7** cats.   12

5 **5** cars and **6** bikes.   11

How many now? There are

6 **15** biscuits and **8** are eaten.   7

7 **19** grapes and **10** are eaten.   9

8 **14** boys and **6** go home.   8

9 **17** birds and **8** fly away.   9

10 **14** crows and **5** fly away.   9

11

Section 1   Session 8

A | ANSWER

1 (15) + •• ••• = **20**

2 13 + ☐ = 20 | **7**

3 19 + ☐ = 20 | **1**

4 ☐ + 16 = 20 | **4**

5 ☐ + 9 = 20 | **11**

6 (20) – ••• = **17**

7 (20) – •••• •••• = **12**

8 (20) – •• •• = **16**

9 (20) – •••• ••• = **13**

10 20 – 14 = **6**

B | ANSWER

1 20 subtract **8** is | **12**

2 20 subtract **4** is | **16**

3 20 subtract **9** is | **11**

4 ☐ add **5** makes **20**. | **15**

5 ☐ and **7** equals **20**. | **13**

6 ☐ add **3** equals **20**. | **17**

7 **20** take away **6** is | **14**

8 **20** minus **2** is | **18**

9 **1** and ☐ equals **20**. | **19**

10 **18** and ☐ equals **20**. | **2**

C | ANSWER

Write how much is left from **20cm** of tape when you cut off

1 **4cm**. | **16cm**

2 **9cm**. | **11cm**

3 **8cm**. | **12cm**

4 **13cm**. | **7cm**

5 **11cm**. | **9cm**

6 **5cm**. | **15cm**

7 **14cm**. | **6cm**

8 **2cm**. | **18cm**

9 **7cm**. | **13cm**

10 **19cm**. | **1cm**

Section 1   Session 9

A
ANSWER

1	10×2	=	20
2	8×2	=	16

3	3×2	=	6
4	5×2	=	10
5	7×2	=	14
6	4×2	=	8
7	6×2	=	12

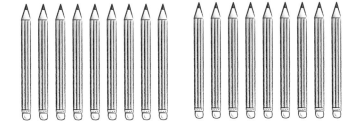

8	9×2	=	18
9	1×2	=	2

10	2×2	=	4

B
ANSWER

1	$14 \div 2$	=	7
2	$18 \div 2$	=	9
3	$6 \div 2$	=	3
4	$12 \div 2$	=	6
5	$16 \div 2$	=	8
6	$4 \div 2$	=	2
7	$20 \div 2$	=	10
8	$2 \div 2$	=	1
9	$16 \div 2$	=	8
10	$10 \div 2$	=	5

C
ANSWER

1	$\quad \times 2 = 4$		2
2	$\quad \div 2 = 8$		16
3	$\quad \times 2 = 10$		5
4	$\quad \div 2 = 10$		20
5	$\quad \times 2 = 14$		7
6	$\quad \div 2 = 6$		12
7	$\quad \times 2 = 20$		10
8	$\quad \div 2 = 5$		10
9	$\quad \times 2 = 18$		9
10	$\quad \div 2 = 7$		14

Section 1 Session 10

Session Focus
Multiplication and division facts for 2s

A
ANSWER

1	5 × 2	=	10
2	7 × 2	=	14
3	9 × 2	=	18
4	6 × 2	=	12
5	3 × 2	=	6
6	16 ÷ 2	=	8

7	20 ÷ 2	=	10
8	12 ÷ 2	=	6

9	4 ÷ 2	=	2
10	14 ÷ 2	=	7

B
ANSWER

What is

1	7 times 2?	14
2	8 divided by 2?	4

3	12 shared by 2?	6
4	4 multiplied by 2?	8
5	the product of 9 and 2?	18
6	6 divided by 2?	3
7	6 multiplied by 2?	12
8	4 divided by 2?	2
9	16 divided by 2?	8
10	the product of 5 and 2?	10

C
ANSWER

1	20 cakes shared between 2 plates.	10
2	18 grapes divided into 2 piles.	9
3	16 cakes shared between 2 plates.	8
4	2 plates with 6 cakes each.	12
5	2 plates with 8 oranges each.	16
6	14 cakes shared between 2 plates.	7
7	2 plates with 4 bananas each.	8
8	2 bags with 10 marbles each.	20
9	2 bags with 5 marbles each.	10
10	10 apples divided into 2 piles.	5

Section 1 Session 11

Session Focus
Read and write numbers to 1000 in figures and words. Sequences of numbers.
Order two-digit numbers and position them on a number line
Use symbols < and >
Add and subtract a two-digit number and a one-digit number

A   ANSWER

Write in figures.

1 Six hundred and two   602

2 Four hundred and twenty   420

3 **15   25   35   45**   55

4 **98   96   94   92**   90

5 Write **36** on the number line.

30   36   40

6 Write **64** on the number line.

60   64   70

Write < or >.

7 **72   27**   >

8 **23   32**   <

9 **56 + 4**   =   60

10 **63 – 4**   =   59

B   ANSWER

Write in words.

1 **654**

six hundred and fifty-four

2 **903**

nine hundred and three

Where do you land if you make

3 **5** jumps of **2** from **20**?   30

4 **6** jumps of **5** from **15**?   45

5 Which is larger, **64** or **67**?   67

6 Which is smaller, **56** or **65**?   56

Use **43** or **34** to answer these two questions.

7 **35 >**   34

8   **< 53**   43

9 Add **47** and **8**.   55

10 What is the difference
between **46** and **8**?   38

C   ANSWER

What is the number

1 after **799**?   800

2 before **600**?   599

3 Start on **18**.
Jump **3** fives.   33

4 Start on **64**.
Jump back **4** tens.   24

5 **89,   , 91**   90

6 **62,   , 58**   60

7 Which is larger, **64** or **65**?   65

8 Which is smaller, **94** or **49**?   49

9 **64** roses and **7** daisies total   71

10 There were **72** marbles
and **5** rolled away.
How many were left?   67

Section 1   Session 12

Session Focus
Add and subtract a two-digit number to/from a multiple of ten
Addition and subtraction for numbers to 20
Multiplication and division facts for 2s

A | ANSWER

1	23 + 8	=	31
2	36 – 8	=	28
3	94 – 7	=	87
4	16 + ⬚ = 20		4
5	⬚ + 3 = 20		17
6	8 + ⬚ = 20		12
7	5 + 4	=	9
8	9 + 1	=	10
9	4 × 2	=	8
10	8 × 2	=	16

B | ANSWER

1	19 add 4.		23
2	87 – 6	=	81
3	39 + 9	=	48
4	⬚ + 9 = 20		11
5	20 take away 5.		15
6	20 subtract 14.		6
7	3 + ⬚ = 10		7
8	8 – 5	=	3
9	7 × 2	=	14
10	18 ÷ 2	=	9

C | ANSWER

What is

1 forty-eight add seven?

fifty-five

2 eighty-six subtract nine?

seventy-seven

3 thirty-two subtract seven?

twenty-five

What is the change from **20p** if you spend

4	8p?	12p
5	9p?	11p
6	What is the change from **10p** if you spend **8p**?	2p

How much is

7	6p add 3p?	9p
8	two lots of 9p?	18p
9	16p shared by 2?	8p
10	10p shared by 2?	5p

Section 2 Group record sheet

Class _____

Name	Read numbers on scales marked in 2s and 5s\n\nSessions 1 and 2	Multiplication and division facts for 5s\n\nSessions 1 and 2	Missing number sentences for addition and subtraction\n\nSession 3	Pairs to total 20\n\nSession 3	Pairs of multiples of 10 to make 100\n\nSession 7	Doubles of all numbers to 20 and matching halves\n\nSession 7

Section 2   Session 1

Session Focus
Read numbers on scales marked in 2s
Multiplication facts for 5s

A ANSWER

Write the number where the arrow points.

1
0 2 4 6 8 10 | 7 |

2
20 22 24 26 28 30 | 25 |

3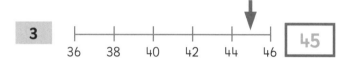
36 38 40 42 44 46 | 45 |

4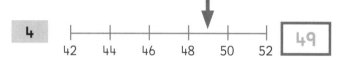
42 44 46 48 50 52 | 49 |

5	**10 × 5**	=	50
6	**6 × 5**	=	30
7	**3 × 5**	=	15
8	**8 × 5**	=	40
9	**7 × 5**	=	35
10	**1 × 5**	=	5

B ANSWER

Write the number where the arrow points.

1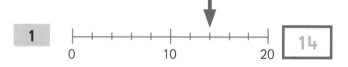
0 10 20 | 14 |

2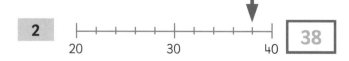
20 30 40 | 38 |

3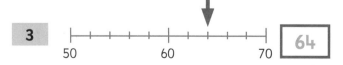
50 60 70 | 64 |

What is

4	**4** multiplied by **5**?	20
5	**9** multiplied by **5**?	45
6	**5** lots of **4**?	20
7	**1** times **5**?	5
8	**10** multiplied by **5**?	50
9	**2** times **5**?	10
10	**5** multiplied by **5**?	25

C ANSWER

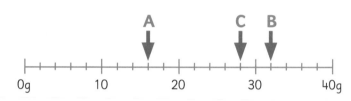
0g 10 20 30 40g

1	Arrow **A** points to	16g
2	Arrow **B** points to	32g
3	Arrow **C** points to	28g

5 apples

How many apples in

4	**6** packs?	30
5	**8** packs?	40
6	**10** packs?	50
7	**4** packs?	20
8	**2** packs?	10
9	**7** packs?	35
10	**9** packs?	45

18

Section 2   Session 2

Session Focus
Read numbers on scales marked in 5s
Division facts for 5s

A   ANSWER

For questions **1** to **3**, write the number that the arrow points to.

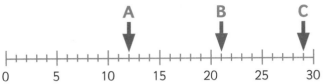

1	**A**	12
2	**B**	21
3	**C**	29
4	**15 ÷ 5** =	3
5	**45 ÷ 5** =	9
6	**30 ÷ 5** =	6
7	**20 ÷ 5** =	4
8	**10 ÷ 5** =	2
9	**35 ÷ 5** =	7
10	**5 ÷ 5** =	1

B   ANSWER

For questions **1** to **3**, write the number that the arrow points to.

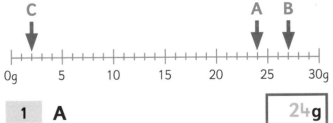

1	**A**	24g
2	**B**	27g
3	**C**	2g
4	**25 ÷ 5** =	5
5	**☐ ÷ 5 = 4**	20

6	☐ **÷ 5 = 6**		30
7	☐ **÷ 5 = 9**		45
8	☐ **÷ 5 = 1**		5
9	**35 ÷ 5**	=	7
10	**40 ÷ 5**	=	8

C   ANSWER

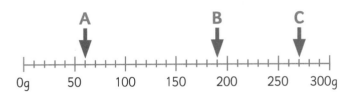

Write how many grams the arrow points to.

1	**A**	60g
2	**B**	190g
3	**C**	270g

Write how many on each plate.

4	**50** oranges shared between **5** plates.	10
5	**35** oranges shared between **5** plates.	7
6	**20** oranges shared between **5** plates.	4
7	**10** oranges shared between **5** plates.	2
8	**15** oranges shared between **5** plates.	3
9	**45** oranges shared between **5** plates.	9
10	**30** oranges shared between **5** plates.	6

Section 2 Session 3

Session Focus
Missing number sentences for addition and subtraction
Pairs to total 20

A   ANSWER

1   ☐ + 5 = 8   3

2   9 + ☐ = 14   5

3   16 + ☐ = 23   7

4   24 + ☐ = 32   8

5   37 + ☐ = 46   9

6   5 + ☐ = 20   15

7   19 + ☐ = 20   1

8   13 + ☐ = 20   7

9   8 + ☐ = 20   12

10 4 + ☐ = 20   16

B   ANSWER

1   42 – ☐ = 38   4

2   63 – ☐ = 59   4

3   71 – ☐ = 62   9

4   84 – ☐ = 78   6

5   ☐ – 7 = 63   70

6   20 – 14 = ☐   6

7   20 – 18 = ☐   2

8   20 – 9 = ☐   11

9   20 – ☐ = 17   3

10 20 – ☐ = 16   4

C   ANSWER

45 apples

You have **45** apples.

Write how many are left when you sell

1   **5** apples.   40

2   another **6** apples.   34

3   another **9** apples.   25

4   another **8** apples.   17

5   another **7** apples.   10

20 oranges

You have **20** oranges.

Write how many are left when you sell

6   **6**   14

7   **9**   11

8   **14**   6

9   **19**   1

10 **0**   20

Section 2 Session 4

Session Focus
Missing number sentences for addition and subtraction
Pairs to total 20

A

ANSWER

1 (9) + •• = $\boxed{13}$

2 16 + __ = 23 $\boxed{7}$

3 24 + __ = 32 $\boxed{8}$

4 __ + 7 = 54 $\boxed{47}$

5 __ + 9 = 51 $\boxed{42}$

6 (19) + ● = __ $\boxed{20}$

7 16 + __ = 20 $\boxed{4}$

8 3 + __ = 20 $\boxed{17}$

9 __ + 8 = 20 $\boxed{12}$

10 __ + 2 = 20 $\boxed{18}$

B

ANSWER

1 36 – __ = 29 $\boxed{7}$

2 45 – __ = 37 $\boxed{8}$

3 94 – 7 = __ $\boxed{87}$

4 __ – 2 = 89 $\boxed{91}$

5 __ – 7 = 63 $\boxed{70}$

6 20 – __ = 15 $\boxed{5}$

7 20 – 9 = __ $\boxed{11}$

8 20 – __ = 14 $\boxed{6}$

9 20 – __ = 0 $\boxed{20}$

10 20 – __ = 2 $\boxed{18}$

C

ANSWER

96 apples

Write each time how many apples are left when you

1 take away **8** apples. $\boxed{88}$

2 eat another **3** apples. $\boxed{85}$

3 sell another **9** apples. $\boxed{76}$

4 give away another **7** apples. $\boxed{69}$

5 sell another **6** apples. $\boxed{63}$

Write how many are left when you have

6 **20** apples and eat **6**. $\boxed{14}$

7 **20** oranges and sell **13**. $\boxed{7}$

8 **20** bananas and eat **2**. $\boxed{18}$

9 **20** pears but **5** are bad. $\boxed{15}$

10 **20** mangoes and sell **4**. $\boxed{16}$

Section 2　Session 5

Session Focus
Multiplication and division facts for 5s

A　　ANSWER

| 1 | 5 × 5 | = | 25 |
| 2 | 7 × 5 | = | 35 |

3	3 × 5	=	15
4	6 × 5	=	30
5	10 × 5	=	50
6	20 ÷ 5	=	4
7	15 ÷ 5	=	3
8	10 ÷ 5	=	2
9	25 ÷ 5	=	5
10	40 ÷ 5	=	8

B　　ANSWER

What is

1	6 multiplied by 5?	30
2	8 multiplied by 5?	40
3	4 times 5?	20

4	9 times 5?	45
5	5 lots of 10?	50
6	30 divided by 5?	6
7	40 divided by 5?	8
8	5 shared by 5?	1
9	35 shared by 5?	7
10	15 shared by 5?	3

C　　ANSWER

Write the answer.

1	25 oranges shared between 5 bowls.	5
2	9 boxes of 5 cakes.	45
3	50 biscuits shared between 5 plates.	10
4	6 boxes of 5 biscuits.	30
5	35 grapes shared between 5 children.	7
6	20 raisins shared between 5 children.	4
7	5 packs of 5 pencils.	25
8	3 bags of 5 apples.	15
9	40 cherries shared between 5 bowls.	8
10	10 bananas shared between 5 people.	2

Section 2　Session 6

Session Focus
Multiplication and division facts for 5s

A

				ANSWER
1	9 ×	**5p**	=	45p
2	3 ×	**5p**	=	15p
3	2 ×	**5p**	=	10p
4	8 ×	**5p**	=	40p
5	10 ×	**5p**	=	50p
6	7 ×	**5p**	=	35p
7	6 ×	**5p**	=	30p
8	1 ×	**5p**	=	5p
9	4 ×	**5p**	=	20p
10	5 ×	**5p**	=	25p

B

			ANSWER
1	$35 \div 5$	=	7
2	$20 \div 5$	=	4
3	$50 \div 5$	=	10
4	$10 \div 5$	=	2
5	$40 \div 5$	=	8
6	$15 \div 5$	=	3
7	$25 \div 5$	=	5
8	$45 \div 5$	=	9
9	$30 \div 5$	=	6
10	$5 \div 5$	=	1

C

		ANSWER
1	How many fives in **40**?	8
2	How many fives in **25**?	5
3	What is **7** times **5**?	35
4	What is **5** lots of **8**?	40
5	How many fives in **50**?	10
6	How many fives in **35**?	7
7	What is **9** times **5**?	45
8	What is **3** multiplied by **5**?	15
9	What is **6** multiplied by **5**?	30
10	How many fives in **15**?	3

Section 2　Session 7

Session Focus
Pairs to total 20
Pairs of multiples of 10 to make 100
Doubles of all numbers to 20 and matching halves

A　　　　　　　　　　　　　　ANSWER

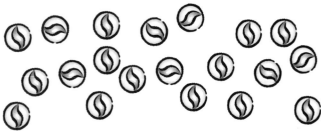

1	19 + ☐ = 20	1
2	☐ + 7 = 20	13
3	6 + ☐ = 20	14

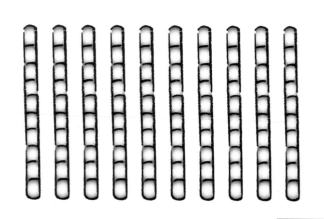

4	30 + 70 = ☐	100
5	10 + ☐ = 100	90
6	50 + ☐ = 100	50
7	14 + 14 = ☐	28
8	20 + 20 = ☐	40
9	16 + 16 = ☐	32
10	13 + 13 = ☐	26

B　　　　　　　　　　　　　　ANSWER

| 1 | 20 − ☐ = 12 | 8 |
| 2 | 20 − ☐ = 2 | 18 |

3	20 − ☐ = 3	17
4	100 − ☐ = 30	70
5	100 − ☐ = 60	40
6	100 − ☐ = 20	80

What is half of

7	30?	15
8	28?	14
9	36?	18
10	38?	19

C　　　　　　　　　　　　　　ANSWER

1	You have **16**. How many more to make **20**?	4
2	Add ☐ to **17** to make **20**.	3
3	**1** and ☐ makes **20**.	19
4	Add ☐ to **30** to total **100**.	70
5	Subtract ☐ from **100** to leave **20**.	80
6	Subtract ☐ from **100** to leave nothing.	100
7	Share **34** between **2**.	17
8	Share **26** between **2**.	13
9	Share **24** between **2**.	12
10	Share **30** between **2**.	15

Section 2   Session 8

Session Focus
Pairs of multiples of 10 to make 100
Doubles of all numbers to 20 and matching halves

A   ANSWER

1   **20 +** ___ **= 100** | 80 |

2   **60 +** ___ **= 100** | 40 |

3   ___ **+ 90 = 100** | 10 |

4   ___ **+ 40 = 100** | 60 |

5   ___ **+ 30 = 100** | 70 |

What is double

6   **15?** | 30 |

7   **19?** | 38 |

8   **11?** | 22 |

9   **17?** | 34 |

10 **16?** | 32 |

B   ANSWER

1   **100 – 80**   **=** | 20 |

2   **100 – 40**   **=** | 60 |

3   **100 – 50**   **=** | 50 |

4   **100 – 70**   **=** | 30 |

5   **100 – 10**   **=** | 90 |

What is half of

6   **40?** | 20 |

7   **36?** | 18 |

8   **28?** | 14 |

9   **32?** | 16 |

10 **22?** | 11 |

C   ANSWER

Write how many eggs are left if you have **100** eggs and sell

1   **40**. | 60 |

2   **70**. | 30 |

3   **50**. | 50 |

4   **80**. | 20 |

5   **10**. | 90 |

Peter	19
Ali	34
Mairi	22
Sam	40
Toni	14

What is

6   double Peter's score? | 38 |

7   half of Ali's score? | 17 |

8   half of Mairi's score? | 11 |

9   half of Sam's score? | 20 |

10 double Toni's score? | 28 |

25

Section 2 Session 9

Session Focus
Pairs of multiples of 10 to make 100
Doubles of all numbers to 20 and matching halves

A

		ANSWER
1	20 + ☐ = 100	80
2	30 + ☐ = 100	70
3	60 + ☐ = 100	40
4	☐ + 70 = 100	30
5	☐ + 90 = 100	10

What is double

6	19?	38
7	14?	28
8	17?	34
9	18?	36
10	12?	24

B

		ANSWER
1	Add ☐ to 30 to make 100.	70
2	Add ☐ to 90 to make 100.	10
3	Add ☐ to 50 to make 100.	50
4	100 subtract ☐ leaves 20.	80
5	100 subtract ☐ leaves 40.	60

What is half of

6	38?	19
7	26?	13
8	32?	16
9	20?	10
10	34?	17

C

		ANSWER

You have **100** oranges.

How many are left if you sell

1	40?	60
2	70?	30
3	20?	80
4	30?	70
5	10?	90

14 apples
30 pears
18 bananas
32 mangoes
40 plums

How many is

6	double the apples?	28
7	half of the pears?	15
8	double the bananas?	36
9	half of the mangoes?	16
10	half of the plums?	20

Section 2 Session 10

A   ANSWER

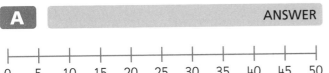

1	**6 × 5**	**=**	30
2	**9 × 5**	**=**	45
3	**4 × 5**	**=**	20
4	**7 × 5**	**=**	35
5	**3 × 5**	**=**	15

4	**35** divided by **5**?	7
5	**5** lots of **2**?	10
6	**25** divided by **5**?	5
7	**9** multiplied by **5**?	45
8	**4** times **5**?	20
9	**5** shared by **5**?	1
10	**15** divided by **5**?	3

6	**25 ÷ 5**	**=**	5
7	**50 ÷ 5**	**=**	10
8	**40 ÷ 5**	**=**	8
9	**10 ÷ 5**	**=**	2
10	**5 ÷ 5**	**=**	1

C   ANSWER

How many marbles?

1	**9** bags of **5** marbles.	45
2	**50** marbles shared by **5**.	10
3	**35** marbles divided by **5**.	7
4	**4** bags of **5** marbles.	20
5	**8** lots of **5** marbles.	40
6	**20** marbles shared between **5**.	4
7	**10** marbles divided into **5** sets.	2
8	**30** marbles shared by **5**.	6
9	**5** lots of **5** marbles.	25
10	**3** bags of **5** marbles.	15

B   ANSWER

What is

1	**40** divided by **5**?	8
2	**10** multiplied by **5**?	50
3	**6** times **5**?	30

Section 2 Session 11

Session Focus
Read numbers on scales marked in 5s
Multiplication and division facts for 5s
Missing number sentences for addition and subtraction

A · ANSWER

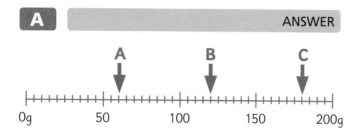

A   B   C

0g   50   100   150   200g

For questions 1 to 3, write where the arrow points.

1	A		60g
2	B		120g
3	C		180g
4	5 × 5	=	25
5	9 × 5	=	45
6	15 ÷ 5	=	3
7	30 ÷ 5	=	6
8	13 + ☐ = 20		7
9	23 − ☐ = 19		4
10	45 + ☐ = 65		20

B · ANSWER

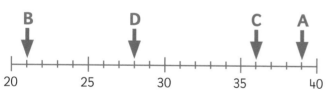

B   D   C   A

20   25   30   35   40

Arrows pointing to the following

1	Where does arrow A point?	39
2	Where does arrow B point?	21
3	Where does arrow C point?	36
4	Where does arrow D point?	28
5	Multiply 8 by 5.	40
6	Divide 50 by 5.	10

What is

7	5 lots of 2?	10
8	35 divided by 5?	7
9	☐ + 7 = 43	36
10	☐ − 8 = 44	52

C · ANSWER

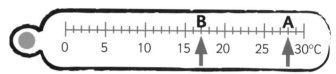

B   A

0   5   10   15   20   25   30°C

Write where the arrows point.

| 1 | A | 28°C |
| 2 | B | 17°C |

How many?

3	9 boxes of 5 pencils.	45
4	4 boxes of 5 pens.	20
5	40 pencils shared between 5 boxes.	8
6	30 pens shared between 5 boxes.	6

Take away each time. Write the answer.

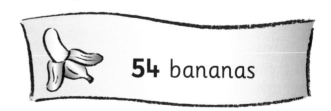

54 bananas

7	Eat 5 bananas.	49
8	Eat 9 more bananas.	40
9	20 bananas sold.	20
10	16 were left. How many more were eaten?	4

Section 2 Session 12

Session Focus
Pairs to total 20
Pairs of multiples of 10 to make 100
Doubles of all numbers to 20 and matching halves

A   ANSWER

1	15 + ☐ = 20	5
2	6 + ☐ = 20	14
3	13 + ☐ = 20	7
4	60 + ☐ = 100	40
5	30 + ☐ = 100	70
6	80 + ☐ = 100	20
7	14 + 14 = ☐	28
8	19 + 19 = ☐	38
9	13 + 13 = ☐	26
10	15 + 15 = ☐	30

B   ANSWER

1	20 – 14 =	6
2	20 – 8 =	12
3	20 – 19 =	1
4	100 – 30 =	70
5	100 – 10 =	90
6	100 – 80 =	20

What is half of

7	38?	19
8	26?	13
9	32?	16
10	22?	11

C   ANSWER

How many more to make **20** if you start with

1	16?	4
2	12?	8
3	3?	17

How many more to make **100** if you start with

4	20?	80
5	90?	10
6	50?	50
7	40?	60

15 marbles
12 tennis balls
38 footballs

What is double the number of

8	marbles?	30
9	tennis balls?	24
10	What is half the number of footballs?	19

Section 3 Group record sheet

Class _____

Name	Halves, quarters and three-quarters of numbers and shapes Session 1	Time Session 2	Read numbers on scales marked in 5s and 10s Session 3	Multiplication and division facts for 2s, 5s and 10s Session 3	Addition and subtraction Session 6

From: **First Mental Arithmetic 6 Answers** by Ann Montague-Smith (ISBN 978 07217 1174 4). Copyright © Schofield & Sims Ltd, 2011. Published by Schofield & Sims Ltd, Dogley Mill, Fenay Bridge, Huddersfield HD8 0NQ, UK (www.schofieldandsims.co.uk). This page may be photocopied for use within your school or institution only.

Section 3 Session 1

A   ANSWER

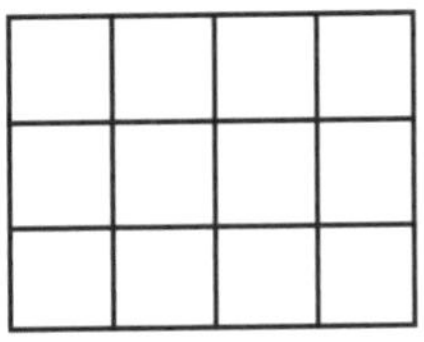

[grid image: 4×3 squares]

Write how many squares.

1	a quarter	3
2	half	6
3	three-quarters	9

What is

4	half of **8**?	4
5	half of **16**?	8
6	a quarter of **20**?	5
7	a quarter of **16**?	4
8	three-quarters of **20**?	15
9	three-quarters of **16**?	12
10	three-quarters of **24**?	18

B   ANSWER

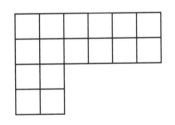

Write how many squares.

1	a quarter	4
2	half	8
3	three-quarters	12

What is

| 4 | half of **32**? | 16 |

5	a quarter of **32**?	8
6	three-quarters of **32**?	24
7	half of **40**?	20
8	a quarter of **40**?	10
9	three-quarters of **40**?	30
10	three-quarters of **8**?	6

C   ANSWER

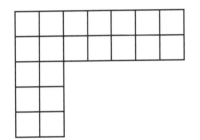

Write how many squares.

1	a half	10
2	a quarter	5
3	three-quarters	15

What is

4	half of a bag of **34** marbles?	17
5	a quarter of a bag of **36** marbles?	9
6	three-quarters of a bag of **36** marbles?	27
7	half of a bag of **28** marbles?	14
8	a quarter of a bag of **28** marbles?	7
9	three-quarters of a bag of **28** marbles?	21
10	three-quarters of a bag of **40** marbles?	30

Section 3 Session 2

A   ANSWER

Write the time for these clocks.

A   B   C

1	A	5.15
2	B	7.30
3	C	9.45
4	How many hours in **1** day?	24
5	How many minutes in half an hour?	30

How many minutes between

| 6 | **5.00** and **5.15**? | 15 |
| 7 | **7.00** and **7.45**? | 45 |

Write the new times. Start with

8	clock **A**. Count on **2** hours.	7.15
9	clock **B**. Count on **2** hours.	9.30
10	clock **C**. Count on **2** hours.	11.45

B   ANSWER

How many

1	hours between noon and midnight?	12
2	minutes between midnight and **2.00**?	120
3	days in a week?	7
4	days in a fortnight?	14

Which day comes

| 5 | after Wednesday? | Thursday |
| 6 | before Wednesday? | Tuesday |

Start at

| 7 | **8.45**. What will be the time in **15** minutes? | 9.00 |
| 8 | midnight. What will be the time in **1** hour? | 1.00 |

Write the time using numbers.

| 9 | half past **8**. | 8.30 |
| 10 | a quarter to **11**. | 10.45 |

C   ANSWER

	Bus A	**Bus B**
Tram Street	9.00	9.15
Town Centre	9.15	9.30

Which bus gets me into town by

1	**9.20**?	A
2	**9.45**?	B
3	How long does the bus journey take?	15 minutes

What time is

4	3 hours from **9.45**?	12.45
5	half an hour after **6.30**?	7.00
6	**15** minutes before **6.45**?	6.30
7	How many minutes between **8.15** and **8.45**?	30

Write the time if you arrive at

8	**9.30** and leave **45** minutes later.	10.15
9	**6.15** and leave **2** hours later.	8.15
10	**8.45** and leave **30** minutes later.	9.15

32

Section 3 Session 3

Session Focus
Read numbers on scales marked in 5s and 10s
Multiplication and division facts for 2s, 5s and 10s

A   ANSWER

Write where the arrow points.

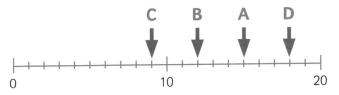

1	A	15
2	B	12
3	C	9
4	D	18

5	7 × 5	=	35
6	3 × 5	=	15
7	2 × 2	=	4
8	9 × 10	=	90
9	8 × 2	=	16
10	1 × 10	=	10

B   ANSWER

Write where the arrow points.

1	A	26
2	B	32
3	C	39
4	D	34

5	40 ÷ 5	=	8
6	18 ÷ 2	=	9
7	30 ÷ 10	=	3
8	30 ÷ 5	=	6
9	80 ÷ 10	=	8
10	14 ÷ 2	=	7

C   ANSWER

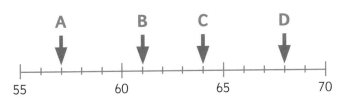

Write where the arrow points.

1	A	57
2	B	61
3	C	64
4	D	68

How many marbles?

5	**6** bags of **10** marbles.	60
6	**70** marbles shared between **10**.	7
7	**18** marbles shared between **2**.	9
8	**2** lots of **8** marbles.	16
9	**7** bags of **5** marbles.	35
10	**50** marbles shared between **5**.	10

33

Section 3   Session 4

A   ANSWER

1	4 × 2	=	8
2	4 × 5	=	20
3	4 × 10	=	40

4	6 × 5	=	30
5	8 × 10	=	80
6	12 ÷ 2	=	6
7	40 ÷ 5	=	8
8	50 ÷ 10	=	5
9	16 ÷ 2	=	8
10	35 ÷ 5	=	7

B   ANSWER

What is

| 1 | 45 divided by 5? | 9 |
| 2 | 4 multiplied by 5? | 20 |

3	14 divided by 2?	7
4	100 shared by 10?	10
5	5 lots of 6?	30
6	× 2 = 12	6
7	× 5 = 25	5
8	× 10 = 90	9
9	÷ 2 = 5	10
10	÷ 5 = 1	5

C   ANSWER

How many?

1	5 bowls of 5 flowers.	25
2	80 flowers put into 10 vases.	8
3	15 roses shared between 5 vases.	3
4	6 boxes of 2 vases.	12
5	10 boxes of 5 bowls.	50
6	9 boxes of 10 bowls.	90
7	50 tulips put into 5 vases.	10
8	20 pansies put into 2 bowls.	10
9	20 pansies put into 5 bowls.	4
10	20 pansies put into 10 bowls.	2

Section 3 Session 5

A

ANSWER

1 $6 \times$ **2p** $=$ | 12p |

2 $8 \div 2$ $=$ | 4 |

3 $4 \times$ **5p** $=$ | 20p |

4 $30 \div 5$ $=$ | 6 |

5 $6 \times$ **10p** $=$ | 60p |

6 $80 \div 10$ $=$ | 8 |

7 3×5 $=$ | 15 |

8 $70 \div 10$ $=$ | 7 |

9 $6 \div 2$ $=$ | 3 |

10 $25 \div 5$ $=$ | 5 |

B

ANSWER

1 $ \times 5 = 35$ | 7 |

2 $ \div 2 = 8$ | 16 |

3 $ \div 10 = 3$ | 30 |

4 $ \div 5 = 9$ | 45 |

5 $ \times 2 = 14$ | 7 |

6 $ \div 10 = 6$ | 60 |

7 $6 \times = 12$ | 2 |

8 $8 \times = 40$ | 5 |

9 $4 \times = 40$ | 10 |

10 $50 \div = 5$ | 10 |

C

ANSWER

1 How many **5p** make **40p**? | 8 |

2 How many **2p** make **16p**? | 8 |

3 How many **10p** make **100p**? | 10 |

4 Divide **60** by **10**. | 6 |

5 Divide **15** by **5**. | 3 |

6 Divide **18** by **2**. | 9 |

7 Share **35** by **5**. | 7 |

8 Share **60** by **10**. | 6 |

9 Share **10p** by **2**. | 5p |

10 What is **8** lots of **5p**? | 40p |

35

Section 3 Session 6

A   ANSWER

1 (5) + :: = 9

2 (15) + :: = 19

3 (18) + :::: = 25

4 (28) + :: = 32

5 (56) + :: = 60

6 (19) – (dots) = 14

7 (22) – :: = 18

8 (36) – (dots) = 27

9 (64) – (dots) = 59

10 (72) – (dots) = 69

B   ANSWER

What is

1 **30** and **23**?   53

2 **46** and **30**?   76

3 **94** minus **40**?   54

4 **64** subtract **50**?   14

5 **30** add **40**?   70

6 the difference between **90** and **50**?   40

7 the difference between **60** and **40**?   20

8 the difference between **30** and **50**?   20

9 **23** subtract **8**?   15

10 **35** minus **7**?   28

C   ANSWER

How much water?

1 **50ml** and another **20ml**.   70ml

2 **100ml** and **70ml** is drunk.   30ml

3 A **15ml** spoonful and a **10ml** spoonful.   25ml

How many books?

4 **48** books. **20** are borrowed.   28

5 **56** books. Another **30** are returned.   86

6 **27** books. Another **4** are returned.   31

7 **31** books. **5** are borrowed.   26

8 **19** books. Another **8** are returned.   27

9 **36** books. **7** books are borrowed.   29

10 **42** books. **6** books are borrowed.   36

Section 3 Session 7

Session Focus
Addition and subtraction

A   ANSWER

1 (16) + ⦂⦂   =   [20]

2 (13) – ⦂⦂   =   [9]

3 [domino] +   =   [14]

4 [domino] +   =   [14]

5 (16) – ⦂⦂⦂   =   [8]

6 (13) + ⦂⦂⦂   =   [20]

7 ☐ + ⦂⦂⦂ = 20   [12]

8 16 + ☐ = 20   [4]

9 14 + ☐ = 20   [6]

10 7 + ☐ = 20   [13]

B   ANSWER

1 ☐ + 5 = 18   [13]

2 ☐ + 9 = 17   [8]

3 11 + ☐ = 16   [5]

4 18 – ☐ = 6   [12]

5 15 – ☐ = 9   [6]

6 ☐ – 11 = 3   [14]

7 20 – ☐ = 14   [6]

8 20 – ☐ = 9   [11]

9 20 – ☐ = 17   [3]

10 20 – ☐ = 5   [15]

C   ANSWER

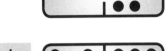

How many if you have

1 16 buns and eat 5?   [11]

2 19 buns and eat 11?   [8]

3 23 buns and eat 8?   [15]

4 15 buns and 6 cakes?   [21]

5 12 buns and 7 cakes?   [19]

6 20 cakes and eat 7?   [13]

7 20 cakes and eat 12?   [8]

8 20 cakes and eat 16?   [4]

9 20 cakes and eat 19?   [1]

10 20 cakes and eat 6?   [14]

Section 3   Session 8

A   ANSWER

1 30 + 40   =   70

2 90 − 50   =   40

3 (64) + ●●●   =   70
            ●

4 (97) − ●●●   =   89
            ●●●
            ●●

5 (13) + ●●●●   =   21
            ●●●●

6 (32) − ●●   =   28
            ●●

7 36 + 40   =   76

8 54 − 30   =   24

9 (12) + ●●●   =   20
            ●●●
            ●●

10 (19) + ●   =   20

B   ANSWER

What is

1 15 add **6**?   21

2 21 subtract **4**?   17

3 the difference between   3
       21 and **18**?

4 the total of **21** and **9**?   30

5 45 minus **5**?   40

6 34 and **30**?   64

7 72 minus **40**?   32

8 20 subtract **8**?   12

9 20 take away **11**?   9

10 20 subtract **18**?   2

C   ANSWER

How many if you have

1 14 grapes and **6** more?   20

2 23 grapes and eat **7**?   16

3 74 pencils and break **5**?   69

4 29 brushes and **7** more?   36

5 64 apples and sell **30**?   34

6 20 grapes and eat **8**?   12

7 20 oranges and sell **4**?   16

8 20 books and give away **13**?   7

How much water?

9 45ml and another **20ml**.   65ml

10 20ml and 11ml more.   31ml

38

Section 3   Session 9

A

ANSWER

1   $6 \times$ **2p**   =   12p

2   $7 \times$ **5p**   =   35p

3   $8 \times$ **10p**   =   80p

4   $1 \times$ **2p**   =   2p

5   $6 \times$ **10p**   =   60p

6   $12 \div 2$ =   6

7   $15 \div 5$ =   3

8   $30 \div 10$ =   3

9   $18 \div 2$ =   9

10   $35 \div 5$ =   7

B

ANSWER

What is

1   **6** multiplied by **5**?   30

2   **7** multiplied by **10**?   70

3   **10** multiplied by **2**?   20

4   **25** divided by **5**?   5

5   **14** divided by **2**?   7

6   **40** divided by **10**?   4

7   **4** times **2**?   8

8   **9** times **5**?   45

9   **50** shared by **10**?   5

10   **2** divided by **2**?   1

C

ANSWER

10 oranges

5 apples

2 pears

Write the totals.

1   **5** boxes of oranges.   50

2   **6** boxes of apples.   30

3   **3** boxes of pears.   6

4   **7** boxes of oranges.   70

5   **8** boxes of pears.   16

6   **9** boxes of apples.   45

7   **10** boxes of oranges.   100

There are

8   **40** oranges. How many boxes?   4

9   **20** apples. How many boxes?   4

10   **4** pears. How many boxes?   2

39

Section 3 Session 10

Session Focus
Multiplication and division facts for 2s, 5s and 10s

A ANSWER

1 3 × **5p** = 15p

2 6 × **5p** = 30p

3 2 × **2p** = 4p

4 12 ÷ 2 = 6

5 15 ÷ 5 = 3

6 50 ÷ 10 = 5

7 7 × **10p** = 70p

8 8 × **2p** = 16p

9 9 × **5p** = 45p

10 30 ÷ 5 = 6

B ANSWER

1 ☐ × 5 = 25 5

2 ☐ × 10 = 90 9

3 ☐ × 2 = 20 10

4 ☐ ÷ 5 = 7 35

5 ☐ ÷ 2 = 9 18

6 ☐ ÷ 10 = 4 40

7 50 ÷ ☐ = 5 10

8 40 ÷ ☐ = 8 5

9 16 ÷ ☐ = 8 2

10 80 ÷ ☐ = 8 10

C ANSWER

Rolls are packed in **5s**.

Cakes are packed in **2s**.

Biscuits are packed in **10s**.

How many packs for

1 **30** rolls? 6

2 **60** biscuits? 6

3 **14** cakes? 7

4 **45** rolls? 9

5 **8** cakes? 4

6 **40** biscuits? 4

7 **20** cakes? 10

8 **35** rolls? 7

9 **60** biscuits? 6

10 **70** biscuits? 7

Section 3　Session 11

Session Focus
Halves, quarters and three-quarters of numbers and shapes
Addition and subtraction

A ANSWER

1 How many squares are half?　7

What is

2 half of **30**?　15

3 a quarter of **20**?　5

4 three-quarters of **12**?　9

5 19 + 7 ＝ 26

6 32 + 8 ＝ 40

7 27 – 6 ＝ 21

8 34 – 8 ＝ 26

9 60 + 30 ＝ 90

10 75 – 40 ＝ 35

B ANSWER

What is

1 a quarter of **40**?　10

2 half of **26**?　13

3 three-quarters of **24**?　18

4 35 + 60 ＝ 95

5 76 – 50 ＝ 26

6 32 – 9 ＝ 23

7 43 + 8 ＝ 51

8 94 – 6　＝ 88

9 13 + 　 = 20　7

10 20 – 　 = 6　14

C ANSWER

How many squares for

1 half?　10

2 a quarter?　5

3 three-quarters?　15

How much water?

4 50ml and 25ml.　75ml

5 35ml and 40ml.　75ml

6 Start with 50ml.
Pour away 30ml.　20ml

7 Start with 65ml.
Pour away 40ml.　25ml

How many?

8 27 books and another 7 books.　34

9 58 cars and 9 cars leave.　49

10 39 motorbikes and 5 more.　44

41

Section 3 Session 12

Session Focus
Read numbers on scales marked in 5s and 10s
Multiplication and division facts for 2s, 5s and 10s
Time
Word problems involving time

A ANSWER

Write the number for each letter.

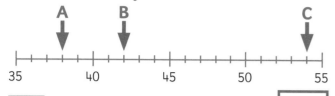

1	**A**	38
2	**B**	42
3	**C**	54
4	**8 × 2**	= 16
5	**8 × 5**	= 40
6	**8 × 10**	= 80

Write the times these clocks show.

7	**A**	9.15
8	**B**	9.45
9	**C**	8.30
10	How many minutes in an hour?	60

B ANSWER

Write the value for each letter.

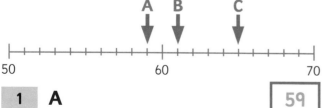

1	**A**	59
2	**B**	61
3	**C**	65

4	**60 ÷ 10**	= 6
5	**20 ÷ 5**	= 4
6	**14 ÷ 2**	= 7
7	**6 × 2**	= 12
8	**9 × 10**	= 90
9	How many minutes in a quarter of an hour?	15
10	Today is Thursday so tomorrow will be	Friday

C ANSWER

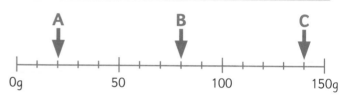

Write the value for each letter.

1	**A**	20g
2	**B**	80g
3	**C**	140g

How many pens?

4	**5** boxes of **10** pens.	50
5	**35** pens shared between **5** boxes.	7
6	**18** pens shared between **2** boxes.	9
7	**6** packs of **2** pens.	12
8	Which day is before Sunday?	Saturday
9	Which day is after Monday?	Tuesday
10	The time is **2.15**. What is the time in **2** hours?	4.15

Check-up 1 Shape and space

A ANSWER

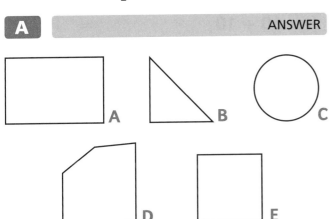

Name these 2D shapes.

1	A	rectangle
2	B	triangle
3	C	circle
4	D	pentagon
5	E	square

Write how many right angles.

6	A	4
7	B	1
8	C	0
9	D	2
10	E	4

B ANSWER

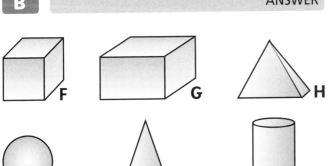

Write the names of the 3D shapes.

1	F	cube
2	G	cuboid
3	H	pyramid
4	I	sphere
5	J	cone
6	K	cylinder

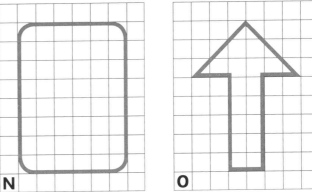

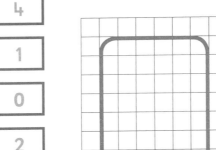

How many right angles inside these shapes?

7	L	5
8	M	6
9	N	0
10	O	3

43

Check-up 2 Handling data

Session Focus
Sorting onto Carroll diagrams
Block graphs

A   ANSWER

These are the numbers **1** to **30**.

	Multiplication facts for **5s**	Not Multiplication facts for **5s**
Multiplication facts for **2s**	10 20 **A**	2 4 6 8 12 14 16 18 22 24 26 **B**
Not multiplication facts for **2s**	5 15 **C**	1 3 7 9 11 13 17 19 21 23 27 **D**

Write the missing numbers.

1	**A**	30
2	**B**	28
3	**C**	25
4	**D**	29

Now the numbers go to **40**.

Write the next number after

5	**A**	40
6	**B**	32
7	**C**	35
8	**D**	31

Write a multiplication fact to go with

9	**A**	6 × 5
10	**C**	5 × 5

B   ANSWER

Here is a block graph.

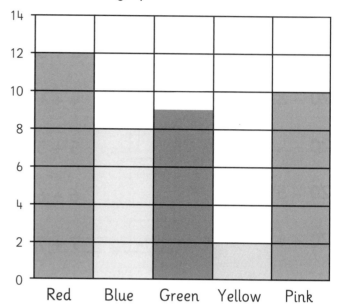

1	Which is the most popular colour?	red
2	Which is the least popular colour?	yellow
3	How many more voted for red than blue?	4
4	How many fewer voted for yellow than green?	7
5	How many voted for red and blue in total?	20
6	How many voted for green and yellow in total?	11
7	How many voted for pink and blue in total?	18
8	Which colour is more popular than pink?	red
9	Which colour is less popular than blue?	yellow
10	How many votes are there altogether?	41

Just facts

20 − 0	=	20	1 + 1	=	2	11 + 11	=	22
20 − 1	=	19	2 + 2	=	4	12 + 12	=	24
20 − 2	=	18	3 + 3	=	6	13 + 13	=	26
20 − 3	=	17	4 + 4	=	8	14 + 14	=	28
20 − 4	=	16	5 + 5	=	10	15 + 15	=	30
20 − 5	=	15	6 + 6	=	12	16 + 16	=	32
20 − 6	=	14	7 + 7	=	14	17 + 17	=	34
20 − 7	=	13	8 + 8	=	16	18 + 18	=	36
20 − 8	=	12	9 + 9	=	18	19 + 19	=	38
20 − 9	=	11	10 + 10	=	20	20 + 20	=	40
20 − 10	=	10						
20 − 11	=	9						
20 − 12	=	8						
20 − 13	=	7						
20 − 14	=	6						
20 − 15	=	5						
20 − 16	=	4						
20 − 17	=	3						
20 − 18	=	2						
20 − 19	=	1						
20 − 20	=	0						

Just facts

Multiplication facts for 2s

1 × 2	=	2
2 × 2	=	4
3 × 2	=	6
4 × 2	=	8
5 × 2	=	10
6 × 2	=	12
7 × 2	=	14
8 × 2	=	16
9 × 2	=	18
10 × 2	=	20

Multiplication facts for 5s

1 × 5	=	5
2 × 5	=	10
3 × 5	=	15
4 × 5	=	20
5 × 5	=	25
6 × 5	=	30
7 × 5	=	35
8 × 5	=	40
9 × 5	=	45
10 × 5	=	50

Multiplication facts for 10s

1 × 10	=	10
2 × 10	=	20
3 × 10	=	30
4 × 10	=	40
5 × 10	=	50
6 × 10	=	60
7 × 10	=	70
8 × 10	=	80
9 × 10	=	90
10 × 10	=	100

Just facts

Division facts for 2s

$2 \div 2$ = 1

$4 \div 2$ = 2

$6 \div 2$ = 3

$8 \div 2$ = 4

$10 \div 2$ = 5

$12 \div 2$ = 6

$14 \div 2$ = 7

$16 \div 2$ = 8

$18 \div 2$ = 9

$20 \div 2$ = 10

Division facts for 5s

$5 \div 5$ = 1

$10 \div 5$ = 2

$15 \div 5$ = 3

$20 \div 5$ = 4

$25 \div 5$ = 5

$30 \div 5$ = 6

$35 \div 5$ = 7

$40 \div 5$ = 8

$45 \div 5$ = 9

$50 \div 5$ = 10

Division facts for 10s

$10 \div 10$ = 1

$20 \div 10$ = 2

$30 \div 10$ = 3

$40 \div 10$ = 4

$50 \div 10$ = 5

$60 \div 10$ = 6

$70 \div 10$ = 7

$80 \div 10$ = 8

$90 \div 10$ = 9

$100 \div 10$ = 10

Full list of the Schofield & Sims First Mental Arithmetic books

Workbooks

First Mental Arithmetic 1	ISBN 978 07217 1163 8
First Mental Arithmetic 2	ISBN 978 07217 1164 5
First Mental Arithmetic 3	ISBN 978 07217 1165 2
First Mental Arithmetic 4	ISBN 978 07217 1166 9
First Mental Arithmetic 5	ISBN 978 07217 1167 6
First Mental Arithmetic 6	ISBN 978 07217 1168 3

Answers

First Mental Arithmetic 1 Answers	ISBN 978 07217 1169 0
First Mental Arithmetic 2 Answers	ISBN 978 07217 1170 6
First Mental Arithmetic 3 Answers	ISBN 978 07217 1171 3
First Mental Arithmetic 4 Answers	ISBN 978 07217 1172 0
First Mental Arithmetic 5 Answers	ISBN 978 07217 1173 7
First Mental Arithmetic 6 Answers	ISBN 978 07217 1174 4

Related materials

The **I can do** teaching method was devised for use at Key Stage 2, with **Schofield & Sims Mental Arithmetic**, and has achieved outstanding results.

This teaching method is equally suitable for use at Key Stage 1, with **First Mental Arithmetic**.

To find out more, watch the film **'I can do maths' in practice** online at **www.schofieldandsims.co.uk/icando/** and order the **I can do maths** Teacher's Guide.

I can do maths Teacher's Guide	ISBN 978 07217 1115 7

All available from

Schofield & Sims Ltd, Dogley Mill, Fenay Bridge, Huddersfield HD8 0NQ

www.schofieldandsims.co.uk

E-mail: sales@schofieldandsims.co.uk
Phone: 01484 607080 Facsimile: 01484 606815